# Skills Practice

## Workbook

**Level K
Book 1**

McGraw Hill SRA

*Columbus, OH*

**SRAonline.com**

 **SRA**

Copyright © 2008 SRA/McGraw-Hill.

All rights reserved. No part of this publication may be
reproduced or distributed in any form or by any means,
or stored in a database or retrieval system, without the
prior written consent of The McGraw-Hill Companies,
Inc., including, but not limited to, network storage or
transmission, or broadcast for distance learning.
An Open Court Curriculum.

Printed in the United States of America.

Send all inquiries to this address:
SRA/McGraw-Hill
4400 Easton Commons
Columbus, OH 43219-6188

ISBN: 978-0-07-610472-7
MHID: 0-07-610472-9

13 14 QLM 16 15

# Table of Contents

## (3) Finding Friends

## (4) By the Sea

## Unit 5 Stick To It

**Name** _____    **Date** _____

Directions: Draw a smiley face in the box just like the one next to the number.

**1.**

**2.**

**3.**

**Name** _____ **Date** _____

**1.**

**2.**

**3.**

**4.**

**5.**

**Name** _____ **Date** _____

Directions: Start at the large dot and follow the dotted line to complete each letter.

**Name** _____ **Date** _____

Directions: Use a crayon to color in any picture that has numbers in it.

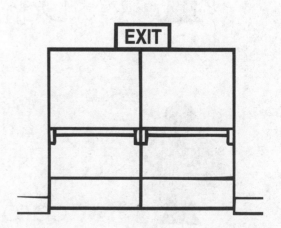

**Name** _____ **Date** _____

Directions: Circle the name that is written correctly with a capital letter.

I.  Anne     anne

2.  adam     Adam

3.  Dan     dan

4.  carol     Carol

**Name** _____ **Date** _____

Directions: Start at the large dot and follow the dotted line to complete each letter.

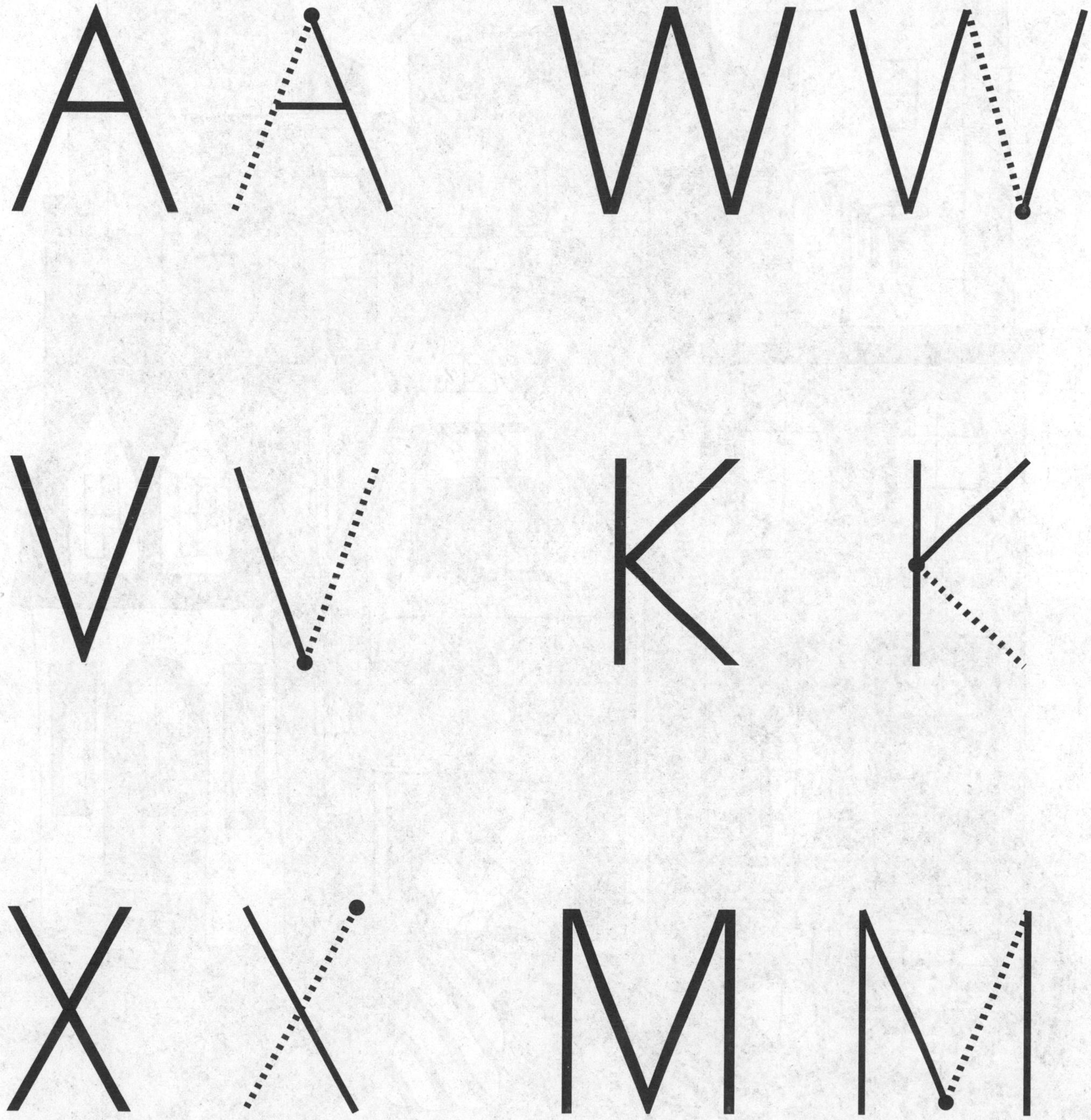

A A W W

V V K K

X X M M

**Name** _____ **Date** _____

Directions: Find and circle capital letters A, B, C, D, E, and F.

**Name** _____  **Date** _____

Directions: Find and circle the small letters *a*, *b*, *c*, *d*, *e*, and *f*.

**Name** _____ **Date** _____

Directions: Draw a circle around the animal in each row.

1.

2.

3.

4.

5.

Words That Name Animals • *Skills Practice 1*

**Name** _____ **Date** _____

Directions: Start at the large dot and follow the dotted line to complete each letter.

**Name** _____ **Date** _____

Directions: Draw a picture of something fun you did yesterday. Sign your name.

**Name** _____ **Date** _____

Directions: Draw a picture of something you would like to bring to class for show and tell.

**Name** _____ **Date** _____

Directions: Draw a circle around the thing in each row.

1.

2.

3.

4.

5.

Words That Name Things • *Skills Practice 1*

**Name** _____  **Date** _____

Directions: Draw a circle around the thing in each row.

1.

2.

3.

4.

5.

**Name** _____  **Date** _____

Directions: Draw a circle around the thing in each row.

I.

2.

3.

4.

5.

**Name** _____ **Date** _____

Directions: Start at the large dot and follow the dotted line to complete each letter.

A A A    N N N

V V V    W W W

X X X    M M M

**Name** _____ **Date** _____

Directions: Draw a circle around the place in each row.

1.

2.

3.

4.

5.

Words That Name Places • *Skills Practice 1*

**Name** _____ **Date** _____

Directions: Draw a line from the capital letter to its matching small letter.

B

D

H

C

I

F

d

b

c

h

i

f

**Name** _____ **Date** _____

Directions: Start at the large dot and follow the dotted line to
complete each letter.

A A N N

V V W W

X X M M

Name _____ Date _____

Directions: Circle the small letter that matches the capital letter.

A    c e a

E    e h l

I    j i l

C    c o e

K    f b k

**Name** _____  **Date** _____

Directions: Connect the dots, in order from A-M, to complete the picture of the bluebird.

Alphabetical Order A-M • *Skills Practice 1*

**Name** _____ **Date** _____

Directions: Circle the picture that matches the word I say.

1. dog

2. ball

3. school

4. boy

5. teacher

6. wagon

7. castle

8. bird

**Name** _____ **Date** _____

**1.**

**2.**

**3.**

**4.**

**5.**

Directions: In each row, color the people—red; animals—blue; things—yellow; and places—green.

**Name** _____ **Date** _____

Directions: Start at the large dot and follow the dotted line to complete each letter.

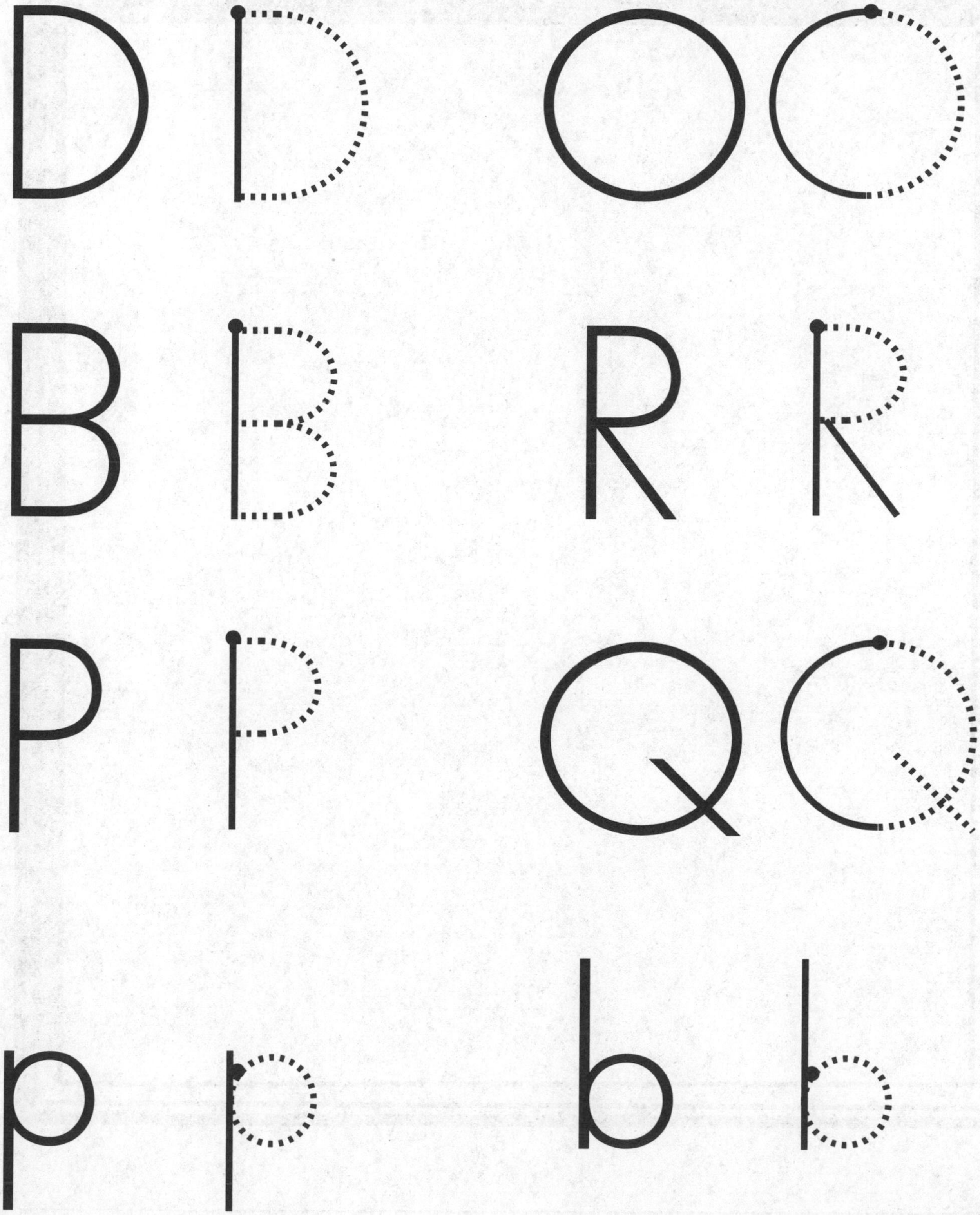

D D
O O
B B
R R
P P
Q Q
p p
b b

**Name** _____ **Date** _____

Directions: Draw what happened first in the fun school event. Remember to sign your name.

**Name** _____ **Date** _____

Directions: Place your pencil on the path where you should begin reading. Follow left to right to complete the maze.

**Name** _____ **Date** _____

Directions: Start at the large dot and follow the dotted line to complete each letter.

C 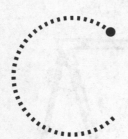 Q

G  d

O  p

e  g

**Name** _____ **Date** _____

Directions: Draw a picture of what happened in the middle of the fun school event. Remember to sign your name.

**Name** _____ **Date** _____

Directions: Draw a picture of what happened at the end of the fun school event. Remember to sign your name.

**Name** _____  **Date** _____

Directions: Circle the picture in each row that matches what I say.

**1.**

**2.**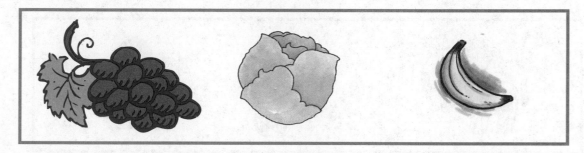

**3.**

**4.**

**Name** _____ **Date** _____

**5.**

**6.**

**7.**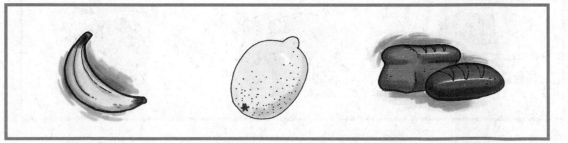

**8.**

Grammar • *Skills Practice 1*

**Name** _____    **Date** _____

Directions: Start at the large dot and follow the dotted line to complete each letter.

**Name** _____  **Date** _____

Directions: Draw a line from the capital letter to its matching small letter.

**Name** _____ **Date** _____

Directions: Draw a line from the action to the object that goes with the action.

**1.**

**2.**

**3.**

**4.**

**5.**

*Skills Practice 1* • Words That Show Action

**Name** _____  **Date** _____

Directions: Circle the picture that shows an action.

6.

7.

8.

9.

10.

Directions: Look at the number on the monkeys' shirts. Draw the correct number of circles inside each basket.

**Name** _____ **Date** _____

Directions: Color the boxes that have a capital Z or a small z.

| E | Z | a | B | h | z |
|---|---|---|---|---|---|
| Y | v | z | t | Z | R |
| f | Z | C | z | g | A |
| Z | T | s | G | e | z |
| b | z | H | c | Z | F |
| S | V | r | Z | y | z |

**Name** _____  **Date** _____

Directions: I will say the word in each row. Circle the picture of the object that has a rhyming name.

1. house

2. toy

3. sat

4. three

5. sing

6. jog

**Name** _____ **Date** _____

Directions: Connect the dots in alphabetical order from N to Z to complete the picture of the willow tree.

**Name** _____ **Date** _____

Directions: Write the capital and small forms of the letter Ss. Write the letter s under the picture whose name begins with the /s/ sound.

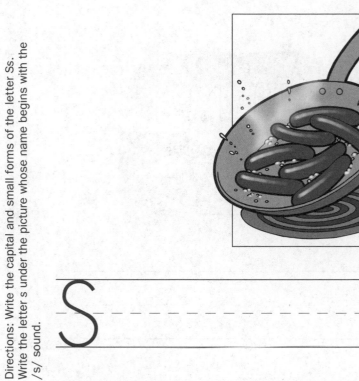

S s

S _ _ _ _ _ _ _ _ _ _ _ _ _ _ _ _ _ _ _ _ _

s _ _ _ _ _ _ _ _ _ _ _ _ _ _ _ _ _ _ _ _ _

_____          _____

_____          _____

**Name** _____ **Date** _____

Directions: Write the letter s under each picture whose name begins with the /s/ sound.

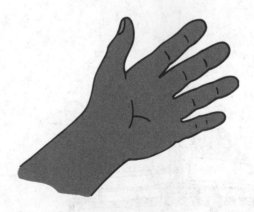

**Name** _____  **Date** _____

**1.** cow

I have a horse.

**2.** Here is the map.

book

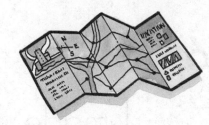

**3.** lion

Elephants are gray.

**4.** My brother has a boat.

table

**Name** _____ **Date** _____

Directions: Listen to the words I read. Circle the sentence.

**5.** This is my house.

cat

**6.** soup

I made the bed.

**7.** sheep

Fish can swim.

**8.** My cat likes yarn.

jam

**Name** _____ **Date** _____

Directions: Write the capital and small forms of the letter *Mm*. Write the letter *m* under the picture whose name begins with the /m/ sound.

M m

M _____

m _____

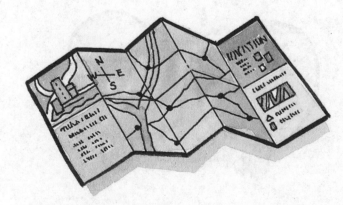

_____

_____

**Name** _____ **Date** _____

Directions: Write the letter m under each picture whose name begins with the /m/ sound.

_____

- - - - - - - - - - - - -

_____

_____

- - - - - - - - - - - - -

_____

**Name** _____   **Date** _____

**1.**  I like dogs.
Ilikedogs.

**2.**  We play games.
Weplaygames.

**3.**  Mycarisred.
My car is red.

**4.**  She walks with me.
Shewalkswithme.

**Name** _____ **Date** _____

Directions: Count the spaces in each sentence, and then circle the correct number of spaces.

**1.** He eats bananas.

1  2

**2.** The cat is sleeping.

2  3

**3.** My mom likes soccer.

3  4

**4.** I have a red ball.

3  4

**Name** _____ **Date** _____

Directions: Write the letter *m* under the picture if it begins with the /m/ sound. Write the letter *s* under the picture if it begins with the /s/ sound.

_____

- - - - - - - - - - - - - -

_____

_____

- - - - - - - - - - - - - -

_____

**Name** _____ **Date** _____

Directions: Write the letter m under the picture if it begins with the /m/ sound. Write the letter s under the picture if it begins with the /s/ sound.

_____

_____

_____

_____

**Name** _____  **Date** _____

D ─────────────────────────────

d ─────────────────────────────

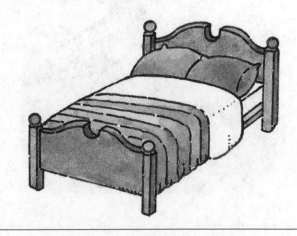

_____  _____

_____  _____

**Name** _____ **Date** _____

Directions: Write the letter *d* under each picture whose name begins with the /d/ sound.

_____     _____

- - - - - - - - - - - - - - - - - -     - - - - - - - - - - - - - - - - - -

_____     _____

_____     _____

- - - - - - - - - - - - - - - - - -     - - - - - - - - - - - - - - - - - -

_____     _____

**Name** _____  **Date** _____

Directions: Write the capital and small forms of the letter *Pp*.
Write the letter *p* under the picture whose name begins with the
/p/ sound.

P p

P _____

p _____

_____

_____

**Name** _____ **Date** _____

Directions: Write the letter *p* under each picture whose name begins with the /p/ sound.

_____

- - - - - - - - - - - - - - - -

_____

_____

- - - - - - - - - - - - - - - -

_____

_____

- - - - - - - - - - - - - - - -

_____

**Name** _____ **Date** _____

Directions: Circle the small letter that matches each capital letter.

 B     b d

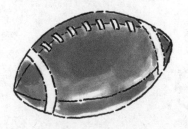 D     b d

F     f h

 H     h b

 M     n m

**Name** _____ **Date** _____

Directions: Circle the small letter that matches each capital letter.

 N  m  n

 P  p  b

 R  r  e

 S  c  s

 T  l  t

Matching Capital and Small Letters • *Skills Practice 1*

**Name** _____ **Date** _____

Directions: Listen as I say each picture name. Write a *d* or *p* to complete each word.

_____ ail

_____ aint

_____ rum

**Name** _____ **Date** _____

Directions: Listen as I say each picture name. Write a d or p to complete each word.

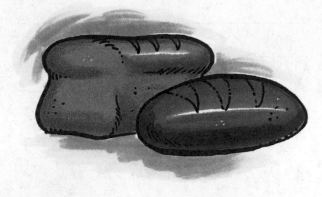

brea

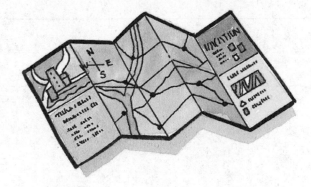

ma

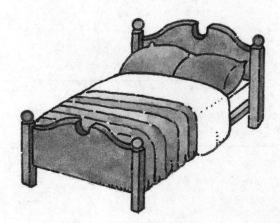

be

Initial and Final Sounds of D and P • *Skills Practice 1*

**Name** _____ **Date** _____

1. The dog ran

2. Apples are red

3. You are nice

4. We saw a cat

5. My bike is red

6. Her bike is new

**Name** _____  **Date** _____

Directions: Trace the capital letter that begins each sentence and add a period at the end of each sentence.

7. The grass is green

8. We go to school

9. A dog barks

10. My cat jumps

11. Horses run fast

12. You can read

**Name** _____ **Date** _____

Directions: Write the capital and small forms of the letter Aa. Write the letter a under the picture whose name has the /a/ sound.

A

a

**Name** _____ **Date** _____

Directions: Write the letter a under each picture whose name has the /a/ sound.

_____

_____

- - - - - - - - - - - - - - -

- - - - - - - - - - - - - - -

_____

_____

_____

_____

- - - - - - - - - - - - - - -

- - - - - - - - - - - - - - -

_____

_____

Identifying Short *A* • *Skills Practice 1*

**Name** _____ **Date** _____

Directions: Circle the word that names each picture.

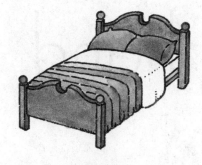

bed          deb

top          pot

hat          tah

spom         mops

**Name** _____  **Date** _____

Directions: Circle the word that names each picture.

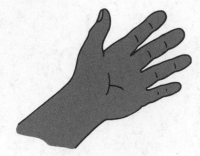  dnah     hand

  tnet     tent

  pond     dnop

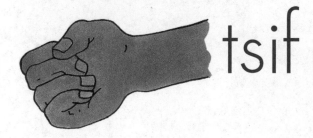  tsif     fist

**Name** _____ **Date** _____

Directions: Circle the objects in the picture whose names have /a/ sound. Write the capital form of the letter Aa.

A

**Name** _____ **Date** _____

Directions: Circle the objects in the picture whose names have /a/ sound. Write the small form of the letter Aa.

a

Identifying Short A • *Skills Practice 1*

**Name** _____ **Date** _____

Directions: Listen as I say each picture name. Write s, m, or a if the word has the /s/, /m/, or /a/ sound.

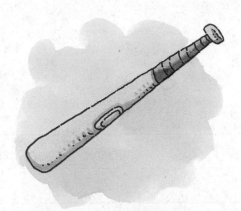

_____
- - - - - - - - - - - - - - - - - - - -
_____

_____
- - - - - - - - - - - - - - - - - - - -
_____

_____
- - - - - - - - - - - - - - - - - - - -
_____

_____
- - - - - - - - - - - - - - - - - - - -
_____

**Name** _____  **Date** _____

Directions: Listen as I say each picture name. Write s, m, or a if the word has the /s/, /m/, or /a/ sound.

can

_____
- - - - - - - - - -
_____

sun

_____
- - - - - - - - - -
_____

mug

_____
- - - - - - - - - -
_____

hat

_____
- - - - - - - - - -
_____

Identifying S, M, and A Sounds • *Skills Practice 1*

**Name** _____ **Date** _____

Directions: Listen as I say each picture name. Write the letter that begins each word. Write an a next to the other letter if the word has the /a/ sound.

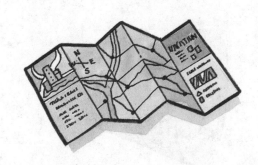

_____

- - - - - - - - - - - - - - - - - -

_____

_____

- - - - - - - - - - - - - - - - - -

_____

_____

- - - - - - - - - - - - - - - - - -

_____

_____

- - - - - - - - - - - - - - - - - -

_____

_____

- - - - - - - - - - - - - - - - - -

_____

_____

- - - - - - - - - - - - - - - - - -

_____

**Name** _____  **Date** _____

Directions: Listen as I say each picture name. Write the letter that ends each word.

_____

- - - - - - - - - - - - - - - -

_____

- - - - - - - - - - - - - - - -

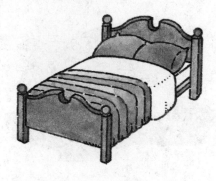

_____

- - - - - - - - - - - - - - - -

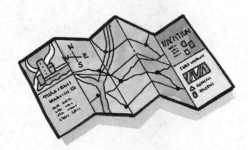

_____

- - - - - - - - - - - - - - - -

_____

- - - - - - - - - - - - - - - -

_____

- - - - - - - - - - - - - - - -

**Name** _____ **Date** _____

Directions: Write the capital and small forms of the letter *Hh*. Write the letter *h* under the picture whose name begins with the /h/ sound.

H    _ _ _ _ _ _ _ _ _ _ _ _ _ _ _ _ _ _ _ _ _ _ _ _

h    _ _ _ _ _ _ _ _ _ _ _ _ _ _ _ _ _ _ _ _ _ _ _ _

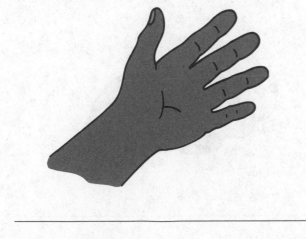

**Name** _____ **Date** _____

Directions: Write the letter *h* under each picture whose name begins with the /h/ sound.

_____

- - - - - - - - - - - - - - - - -

_____


_____

- - - - - - - - - - - - - - - - -

_____

_____

- - - - - - - - - - - - - - - - -

_____


_____

- - - - - - - - - - - - - - - - -

_____

**Name** _____ **Date** _____

Directions: Write the capital and small forms of the letter *Tt*. Write the letter *t* under the picture whose name begins with the /t/ sound.

T

t

**Name** _____ **Date** _____

Directions: Write the letter *t* under each picture whose name begins with the /t/ sound.

_____

- - - - - - - - - - - - - -

_____

_____

- - - - - - - - - - - - - -

_____

_____

- - - - - - - - - - - - - -

_____

_____

- - - - - - - - - - - - - -

_____

**Name** _____  **Date** _____

T t

Directions: Write the capital and small forms of the letter *Tt*. Write the letter *t* under the picture whose name ends with the /t/ sound.

T _____

t _____

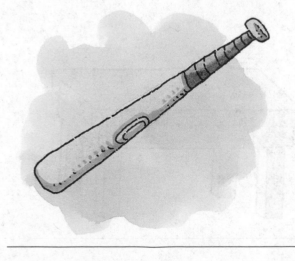

_____

**Name** _____ **Date** _____

Directions: Write the letter *t* under each picture whose name ends with the /t/ sound.

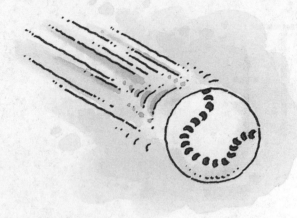

_____

_____

_____

_____

Identifying Final Sound of *T* • *Skills Practice 1*

**Name** _____  **Date** _____

**1.** Do you like to paint?
I like to read.

**2.** Here is my lunchbox.
Do you like to swim?

**3.** Is it raining?
Tara knows how to swim.

**4.** Where is your sock?
The pen is blue.

**5.** This is my mom's car.
Do you ride the school bus?

**Name** _____ **Date** _____

Directions: Listen as I read each sentence. Circle the sentence that asks a question.

**6.** We like to run.

Did you see the ball?

**7.** Are you the teacher?

He is hungry.

**8.** Do you like dogs?

Ben plays soccer.

**9.** Anne likes school.

Where is the book?

**10.** Can I have an apple?

I cleaned my room.

Word to Sentences • *Skills Practice 1*

**Name** _____ **Date** _____

Directions: Listen as I say each picture name. Write an *h* or a *t* to complete each word.

_____
‾ ‾ ‾ ‾ ‾ ‾ ‾ ‾ ‾
am
_____

_____
‾ ‾ ‾ ‾ ‾ ‾ ‾ ‾ ‾
op
_____

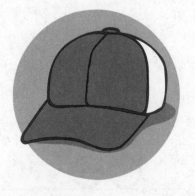

_____
‾ ‾ ‾ ‾ ‾ ‾ ‾ ‾ ‾
at
_____

**Name** _____  **Date** _____

Directions: Listen as I say each picture name. Write an *h* or a *t* to complete each word.

_____ ug

_____ en

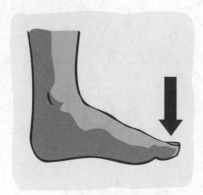

_____ oe

**Name** _____ **Date** _____

Directions: Write the capital and small forms of the letter *Nn*. Write the letter *n* under the picture whose name begins with the /n/ sound.

N

n

**Name** _____ **Date** _____

Directions: Write the letter *n* under each picture whose name begins with the /n/ sound.

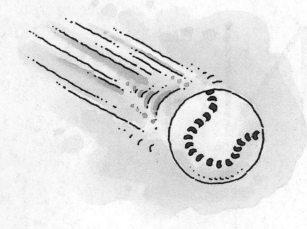

_____

- - - - - - - - - - - - - - - - - - - -

_____

_____

- - - - - - - - - - - - - - - - - - - -

_____

_____

- - - - - - - - - - - - - - - - - - - -

_____

_____

- - - - - - - - - - - - - - - - - - - -

_____

**Name** _____ **Date** _____

Directions: Write the letter *n* under each picture whose name ends with the /n/ sound.

_____
- - - - - - - - - - - - - -
_____

_____
- - - - - - - - - - - - - -
_____

_____
- - - - - - - - - - - - - -
_____

_____
- - - - - - - - - - - - - -
_____

_____
- - - - - - - - - - - - - -
_____

_____
- - - - - - - - - - - - - -
_____

**Name** _____     **Date** _____

Directions: Write the letter *n* under each picture whose name ends with the /n/ sound.

_____

- - - - - - - - - - - - - - - - - - -

_____

_____

- - - - - - - - - - - - - - - - - - -

_____

_____

- - - - - - - - - - - - - - - - - - -

_____

**Name** _____ **Date** _____

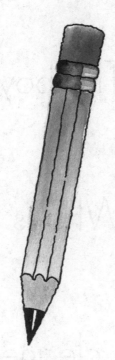

1.  I saw the dog.

2.  Do you like grapes?

3.  Do you see him?

4.  Where did they go?

5.  She likes to play.

6.  How are you?

**Name** _____ **Date** _____

Directions: Listen carefully as I read each sentence. Circle the correct end mark.

**7.** The boy was hungry  .  ?

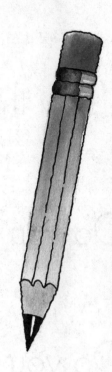

**8.** Who is it  .  ?

**9.** I cleaned my room  .  ?

**10.** The cat ran up the tree  .  ?

**11.** Are you the teacher  .  ?

End Marks • *Skills Practice 1*

**Name** _____  **Date** _____

Directions: Write the capital and small forms of the letter *Ll*.
Write the letter *l* under the picture whose name begins with the /l/ sound.

Ll

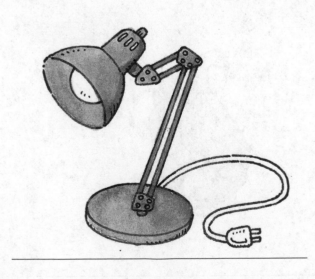

**Name** _____ **Date** _____

Directions: Write the letter *l* under each picture whose name begins with the /l/ sound.

Identifying Initial Sound of *L* • *Skills Practice 1*

Directions: Draw a circle around each object in the picture whose name ends with the /l/ sound. Write the capital form of the letter *Ll*.

**Name** _____  **Date** _____

Directions: Draw a circle around each object in the picture whose name ends with the /l/ sound. Write the small form of the letter Ll.

Identifying Final Sound of *L* • *Skills Practice 1*

**Name** _____     **Date** _____

Directions: Listen as I say each picture name. Write an *n* or an *l* to complete each word.

_____ails

_____et

_____ock

**Name** _____ **Date** _____

Directions: Listen as I say each picture name. Write an *n* or an *l* to complete each word.

pai

te

fa

**Name** _____  **Date** _____

Directions: Listen as I say each picture name. Write the missing letter *i* to complete each word.

nch

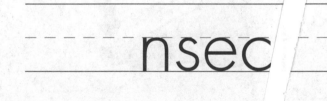
nsec

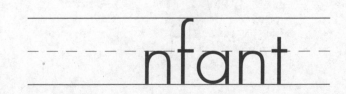
nfant

**Name** _____ **Date** _____

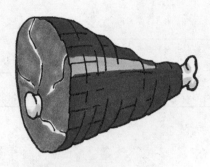

Directions: Listen carefully as I name each picture. Write *h* or *t* under each picture whose name begins with the /h/ or /t/ sound. Write *i* beside the other letter if you hear the /i/ sound.

_____

- - - - - - - - - - - - -

_____

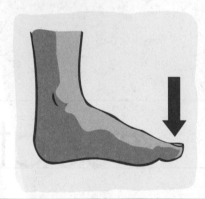

_____

- - - - - - - - - - - - -

_____

_____

- - - - - - - - - - - - -

_____

**Name** _____  **Date** _____

Directions: Listen carefully as I name each picture. Write *h*, *t*, *n*, or *l* under each picture whose name begins with the /h/, /t/, /n/, or /l/ sound. Write *i* beside the other letter if you hear the /i/ sound.

_____

- - - - - - - - - - - - - - - - - - -

_____

_____

- - - - - - - - - - - - - - - - - - -

_____

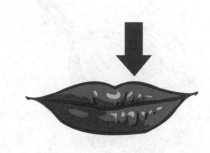

_____

- - - - - - - - - - - - - - - - - - -

_____

_____

- - - - - - - - - - - - - - - - - - -

_____

_____

- - - - - - - - - - - - - - - - - - -

_____

_____

- - - - - - - - - - - - - - - - - - -

_____

**Name** _____  **Date** _____

Directions: Listen carefully as I name each picture. Write h, t, n, or l under each picture whose name ends with the /h/, /t/, /n/, or /l/ sound. Write i beside the other letter if you hear the /i/ sound.

_____

- - - - - - - - - - - -

_____

- - - - - - - - - - - -

_____

- - - - - - - - - - - -

_____

- - - - - - - - - - - -

_____

- - - - - - - - - - - -

_____

- - - - - - - - - - - -

Review • *Skills Practice 1*

**Name** _____  **Date** _____

# Bb

B _____

b _____

_____          _____

Directions: Write the capital and small forms of the letter *Bb*. Write the letter *b* under the picture whose name begins with the /b/ sound.

**Name** _____  **Date** _____

Directions: Write the letter *b* under each picture whose name begins with the /b/ sound.

_____

- - - - - - - - - - - - - - - - - -

_____

_____

- - - - - - - - - - - - - - - - - -

_____

**Name** _____ **Date** _____

Directions: Listen carefully to each sentence I read. Circle the exclamation point.

**1.** Do you like bugs?
Look at that bug!

**2.** Owen plays soccer.
Owen scored a goal!

**3.** Penguins have black and white feathers.
I love penguins!

**4.** We are going to the zoo!
How many animals are there?

**5.** I use glue in art class.
Put those scissors down!

**Name** _____          **Date** _____

Directions: Write the capital and small forms of the letter Cc. Write the letter c under the picture whose name begins with the /k/ sound.

C

C

**Name** _____ **Date** _____

Directions: Write the letter c under each picture whose name begins with the /k/ sound.

_____

— — — — — — — —

_____

_____

— — — — — — — —

_____

_____

— — — — — — — —

_____

_____

— — — — — — — —

_____

**Name** _____  **Date** _____

Directions: Listen carefully as I read each sentence. Circle the correct end mark.

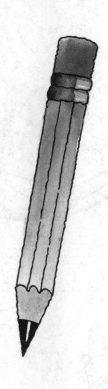

1.  Be quiet now  **?**  **!**

2.  Do you eat spinach  **?**  **!**

3.  The pen is black  **!**  **.**

4.  It is great to see you  **?**  **!**

5.  Do you see the fog  **?**  **!**

6.  This book is so good  **!**  **.**

**Name** _____ **Date** _____

Directions: Circle all pictures whose names end with the /b/ sound. Write the capital form of the letter *Bb* on the line.

B

**Name** _____ **Date** _____

b _ _ _ _ _ _ _ _ _ _ _ _ _ _ _ _ _ _ _ _

**Name** _____ **Date** _____

Directions: Write the capital and small forms of the letter Oo.
Write the letter o under the picture whose name has the /o/ sound.

**Name** _____    **Date** _____

Directions: Write the letter o under each picture whose name has the /o/ sound.

_____

- - - - - - - - - - - - - -

_____

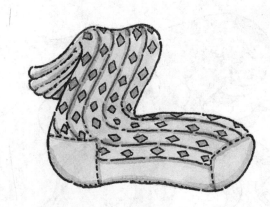

_____

- - - - - - - - - - - - - -

_____

Name ______________________ Date ________

Directions: Listen carefully as I read the words. Circle the time and order word.

1. yesterday talk

2. read tomorrow

3. jump today

4. before listen

5. sleep then

6. after walk

**Name** _____ **Date** _____

Directions: Look at the first circled picture. In each row circle the picture that shows what happens next.

**7.**

**8.**

**9.**

**10.**

Time and Order Words • *Skills Practice 1*

**Name** _____ **Date** _____

Directions: Write the capital and small forms of the letter *Rr*.
Write the letter *r* under the picture whose name begins with the /r/ sound.

# Rr

R _____

r _____

_____     _____

_____     _____

**Name** _____  **Date** _____

Directions: Write the letter r under each picture whose name begins with the /r/ sound.

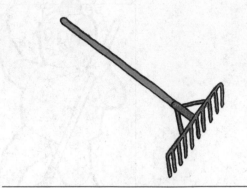

_____

- - - - - - - - - - - - - -

_____

_____

- - - - - - - - - - - - - -

_____

_____

- - - - - - - - - - - - - -

_____

**Name** _____ **Date** _____

Directions: Write the capital and small forms of the letter Gg. Write the letter g under the picture whose name begins with the /g/ sound.

G g

G

g

_____ _____

_____ _____

**Name** _____ **Date** _____

Directions: Write the letter g under each picture whose name begins with the /g/ sound.

_____

- - - - - - - - - - - - - - -

_____

**Name** _____ **Date** _____

pig     tag

_____

rug     bug

_____

pig     fig

_____

bag     hug

_____

**Name** _____  **Date** _____

Directions: Circle the word with the final /g/ sound that names the picture. Then write the letter on each line that makes the /g/ sound.

fog    log

_____

- - - - - - - - - - -

_____

egg    leg

_____

- - - - - - - - - - -

_____

hog    dog

_____

- - - - - - - - - - -

_____

bag    wig

_____

- - - - - - - - - - -

_____

**Name** _____ **Date** _____

bat     hat

_____

- - - - - - - - - -

_____

cat     tot

_____

- - - - - - - - - -

_____

hot     dog

_____

- - - - - - - - - -

_____

pot     drop

_____

- - - - - - - - - -

_____

**Name** _____ **Date** _____

Directions: Write the letter o under each picture whose name has the /o/ sound. Find one picture name that begins with the /k/ sound and write c under it.

_____

- - - - - - - - - - - - - - - -

_____

_____

- - - - - - - - - - - - - - - -

_____

_____

- - - - - - - - - - - - - - - -

_____

**Name** _____ **Date** _____

Directions: Listen carefully as I read each sentence. Circle the letter T if the sentence *tells* something. Circle the letter A if the sentence *asks* something. Circle the letter S if the sentence shows *strong feeling*.

**1.** I have a wagon.  T  A  S

**2.** Have you seen my shoes?  T  A  S

**3.** That is too heavy!  T  A  S

**4.** Have you seen that movie?  T  A  S

**5.** The apple tastes good.  T  A  S

**6.** Horses run fast.  T  A  S

**7.** That looks fun!  T  A  S

**8.** Are you ready to go?  T  A  S

*Skills Practice 1* • Sentence Types

**Name** _____ **Date** _____

Directions: Listen carefully to the directions. After I read the three sentences, I will name a sentence type. Circle the sentence that matches the sentence type I name.

**1.** What color are carrots?

Carrots are orange.

These are good carrots!

**2.** You are here.

Where are you?

Oh, there you are!

**3.** The car zoomed by.

Slow down!

How fast did it go?

**4.** Did you wear a coat?

It is cold.

It is freezing!

Sentence Types • *Skills Practice 1*